First published in Great Britain in 1980 by Andersen
Press Ltd., 3 Fitzroy Square, London, W1. Published
in Australia by Hutchinson of Australia, Richmond,
Victoria 3121. Illustrations © 1980 Ross Thomson.
Text © 1980 Maryann Macdonald. ISBN 0 905478 79 7.
Printed in Italy by Grafiche AZ, Verona.

MOVING, DOING, BUILDING, BEING

Maryann Macdonald

Illustrated by Ross Thomson

Andersen Press/Hutchinson

Walking is
making one foot
keep up with the other.

Running is
doing it
faster.

Tripping is
when one foot
gives up.

Falling is when
both feet do.

Sitting is
what bottoms are for.

Resting is
what you do when
your body is tired.

Sleeping is
what happens
if your mind
is tired too.

Climbing is
one way
of going up.

Jumping is
another.

Flying
is something
only birds can do.

Talking is
telling people
things.

Whispering is doing
it softly.

Listening is being
quiet so you
can hear.

Seeing is what happens
when you open your eyes.

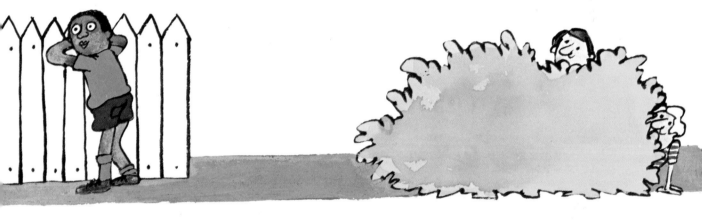

Watching is looking
at something you see.

Drawing is putting ideas on paper with pictures.

Writing is doing the same with words.

Reading is
following the ideas.

Believing
is swallowing
the ideas.

Pushing is
moving something
from
behind.

Pulling is usually harder.

Going is leaving
people and places behind.

Coming is arriving
at new places.

Digging is moving earth from place to place.

Blowing is moving air.

Building is
putting things together
to make something.

Breaking is
smashing it to pieces.

Kicking is
one way of
breaking things.

Dropping is
the usual way.

Dancing is
letting music
into your body.

Singing is letting
it come out
of your mouth.

Crawling is what babies do
but it's sometimes
fun anyway.

Hiding is
being in a secret place.

Finding is
discovering
the secret.

Playing is all of these
things...and more!

Shopping is
buying things.

Eating makes
food into you.

Cooking is making meals out of food.

Washing is cleaning up afterwards.

Working is doing what you have to do.

Drying can happen by itself.

Smiling is what your mouth does when something makes you happy.

Laughing is when happiness comes out in sounds.

Crying is when sadness does the same.

Tickling is a sly,
silly way to
make people laugh.

Kissing
is one way of
showing someone
that you
love them.

Hugging is
holding someone
close.

Having means
caring for
things.

Doing is better.

Being
is best of all.